The Geolog

C000224892

Lake District

an introduction

by Robert Westwood
robert.westwood3@btinternet.com

Inspiring Places Publishing

www.inspiringplaces.co.uk
2 Down Lodge Close
Alderholt
Fordingbridge
Hampshire
SP63JA
ISBN 978-0-9552061-9-1
© Robert Westwood 2009
All rights reserved
Printed by Corvette Printing Ltd., Bournemouth

Cover photograph: Looking towards Derwent Water from the Glenderaterra valley.
Rear cover photograph: Sourmilk Gill near Buttermere.
All photographs by the author.

Contents

Page

Introduction

Many people have fallen in love with the majestic scenery of the Lake District; writers, artists, photographers and walkers have all been drawn there time and time again. It is, perhaps, only fitting that the formation of such a landscape should involve long and complicated processes, as if nature, through arduous and skilled labour, had produced a masterly work of art. The effect is enhanced by the relatively compact and well-defined extent of the Lake District. This book will try to explain some of the processes that have contributed to the evolution of the area and point out the evidence to be seen in the valleys and on the fells, for surely, a little understanding can only enhance an appreciation of the beauty.

We will first need to consider some general principles. The science of geology changed enormously in the latter half of the 20th century following the acceptance of the theory of plate tectonics and the implication that continents were not fixed in position. We now know that the surface of the planet is constantly changing; continents move and oceans are formed and squeezed out of existence. The driving force behind this process comes from heat deep within the Earth, caused by the decay of radioactive elements. It seems that the Earth's crust is divided into a number of plates moving relative to one another under the influence of rising currents of heat. It is along the boundaries of these plates that we see almost all of the planet's volcanic and earthquake activity. Where plates collide there are buckles and corrugations in the crust. On a planetary scale these may seem like minor crumples, but

Left: The wild heart of the Lake District composed of volcanic rocks from a relatively short episode nearly 500 million years ago.

on a human scale they present as mighty mountain ranges and deep sea trenches.

The idea that continents move raises all sorts of conceptual problems. What do they move on? How can solid rock flow? Many geologists were slow to accept the new theory; but that is not now an option. Never mind how it happens, scientists can measure the movement. Modern instruments tell us, for example, that the Atlantic Ocean is widening by a few centimetres each year. A popular analogy is to say that continents move at around the rate your fingernails grow.

As we look at the processes that have formed the Lake District it may help to remember two points. Firstly, scientists have discovered that a layer just below the Earth's crust behaves in a rather fluid manner. This is because of the unique combination of temperature and pressure that the rocks here find themselves under; although it gets hotter towards the centre of the Earth, further down the pressure is too great to allow such fluidity. This may be the layer that allows continental drift. Secondly, rocks behave very differently under heat and intense pressure than they do on the surface. Think of the play material that bends and moulds when massaged in the hands but that shatters if thrown against something hard.

Around 500 million years ago the area we call the Lake District was situated on the boundary where two plates were colliding, deep in the southern hemisphere. The scenario was somewhat similar to the eastern side of the Pacific where the oceanic Pacific plate is colliding with and being forced under [subducted] the Asian plate. Consult an atlas, preferably one that shows submarine topography, and you will see that on and around this coastline are numerous volcanoes and deep sea trenches. It all fits the picture of two slabs of crust moving slowly and inexorably together. It is in fact the oceanic [Pacific] plate that is moving towards the continental [Asian] plate. Why should there be volcanic activity? The answer to this is thought to lie in the friction created when one part of the crust slides underneath another. Some partial melting of the rocks may occur and the resulting molten rock or magma will rise by buoyancy through any cracks and fissures. It may melt other rock on the way and it is easy to appreciate that a variety of magma compositions may result and hence a variety of rock types when the magma cools and solidifies. This is exactly what we find in these areas.

It is not just the wandering of crustal plates that changes the landscape. Atmospheric processes and the oceans weather and erode any part of the crust above sea level, trying to smooth out the surface of the Earth. Much eroded material finds its way into the seas via rivers,

Looking towards Derwent Water from Glenderaterra. The smooth topography of the Skiddaw Group gives way to craggy volcanics.

building up huge quantities of sediment on the sea bed, particularly on the continental shelf bordering the continents. After burial and compaction this sediment will become sedimentary rock. Much of the world's land is covered by such layers that once formed on the sea bed, now raised and perhaps contorted by the restless motion of the plates. They will be eroded again and the cycle will continue as long as the power source deep within the Earth continues. The buckles and trenches that form on the ocean floor between colliding plates provide basins into which thousands of feet of sediment can accumulate. These basins may be separated by ridges and the whole undersea topography may change as the crust accommodates to the huge stresses caused by the relentless advance of the plates. The sequences of sedimentary rocks that form in such environments can often be readily identified. They can, for example, be incredibly thick sequences, as vast piles of detritus collect in the basins or trenches. Sediment can sometimes pile up precariously on the sloping sides of the basins, periodically tumbling into the abyss in a swirling current. Such "turbidity" currents produce sediments with characteristic structures and these have been identified in many places in the Lake District.

This is the background from which we should begin our look at the geology of the Lake District.

The Geological Time Scale

Era	Period	Age[my]
Cenozoic — Quaternary	Neogene	25
	Palaeogene	65
Mesozoic	Cretaceous	145
	Jurassic	200
	Triassic	250
Palaeozoic	Permian	300
	Carboniferous	360
	Devonian	415
	Silurian	445
	Ordovician	490
	Cambrian	550
Pre-Cambrian		4600

Probably the most well-known division of geological time is the period. It is a testament to early British geologists that many of these names stem from the British Isles - although not the Jurassic which gives its name to the mainland's only natural World Heritage Site! The divisions of geological time are based on the fossil record; there are major changes in the record between periods and even more major changes between eras. Almost all life on Earth died out at the end of the Palaeozoic and Mesozoic eras in major global extinctions. The Cambrian period is the first in which we see easily recognisable fossils.

The actual age of rocks is only known from radio-isotope dating. This is not always possible and so there is doubt with some of the ages expressed in geological texts.

Map of Lake District Geology

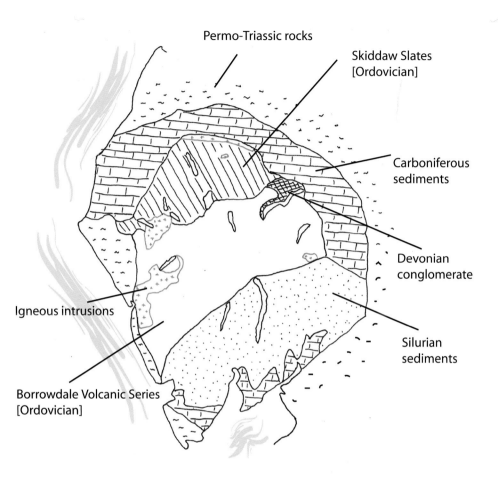

Above is a much simplified map of the solid geology of the Lake
District. Many parts of the area are covered by much more recent drift
deposits from the Ice Age; this is not shown. The central part, largely the
National Park, is composed of three rock formations. These are, in order
of age, oldest first, the Skiddaw Slates, the Borrowdale Volcanic Series
and the Windermere Supergroup [shown here as Silurian sediments].
Note how these rocks are aligned in a roughly SW to NE direction.

The Geological History of the Lake District

Around 500 million years ago in a time geologists have labelled the Ordovician [after an ancient Welsh tribe, the Ordovices] the Lake District was on the edge of a large ocean, perhaps in a situation comparable with the Asian seaboard of the Pacific where an oceanic plate is colliding with a continental plate. For the next hundred million years or so this picture continued. Vast amounts of sediment accumulated in deep basins and on the shallower waters of the continental shelf. Explosive bursts of volcanic activity released huge quantities of lava and ash onto the surface. Volcanoes also led to the development of chains of islands that ran parallel to the ancient coastline. Such volcanic island arcs are typical of destructive plate margins.

A hundred million years is a very long time. Consider the rate of plate movement to be around 5 cm per year; in a hundred million years this equates to a distance travelled of 5000 km! All this was happening well south of the Equator and what was to become England and Wales was on the opposite side of the ocean from NW Scotland. There were probably several subduction zones where one crustal plate slides beneath another and several island arc systems born of volcanic activity.

The oldest Lake District rocks are the Skiddaw Slates. These are mudstones and sandstones that collected in the shelf seas and the deeper basins. There are also "greywackes", sandstones which show the tell-tale structures of sediment that has tumbled down a submarine slope. The slates gained their slaty "cleavage" from subsequent compression, more on that later.

There followed a dramatic and intense period of volcanic activity along the island arc system. It started with relatively sedate outpouring of lava flows but then switched to an altogether more explosive phase. Thousands of metres of lavas, ash and tuff built up, forming huge mountains. Over millions of years these mountains were worn down and the Lake District was again covered by the warm seas. Remember, all life was then to be found in the sea so the bare, arid land was quickly eroded. More sediments accumulated, including limestones. We are now in the Silurian period, again named after an ancient Welsh tribe [the Silures]. The Iapetus Ocean was now much thinner and was being squeezed out of existence as two continental plates continued to converge. Eventually in the Devonian period, nearly 400 million years

Looking across to High Rigg. Composed of volcanic tuffs and lava flows, the harder lava layers stand out and give a stepped appearance.

ago the ocean was closed and the sediments and volcanic rocks were compressed and folded into a huge mountain range, the Caledonides. England and NW Scotland were joined, almost seamlessly, but the famous Moine Thrust is now known to be the boundary where this collision occurred. Deep underneath the mountain chain, intense heat had melted large chunks of the Earth's crust and some of the mantle below it. Some of the melt had migrated upwards, embedding itself within the contorted sediments. These were the granites and other coarse grained igneous rocks we see now exposed at various places in the Lake District; coarse grained because, buried deep underground, they took thousands of years to cool and solidify.

Another period of erosion now followed and after millions of years the mountains were eroded flat. The sea returned again leading to a famous cycle of sedimentary rocks from the Carboniferous period including the Carboniferous limestone and the Coal Measures. Plants had, by now, colonised the land and the rich forests and luxuriant vegetation of coastal swamps have provided us with a valuable fuel.

Glenderaterra Valley cut into the Skiddaw Slates - the eroded core of a once great mountain range.

The valley of the River Caldew - again cut into Skiddaw Slates. The valley has the characteristic U - shape of one that has been widened by a glacier. Just to the north [left of picture] is Carrock Fell, composed of igneous [volcanic] rocks that were once buried deep in the Earth and formed as a result of the heat generated by the collision of tectonic plates. They are now exposed on the surface. Sheets of lava were also intruded into the slates of the Caldew Valley and these can now be seen exposed on the valley floor.

Since then Britain has felt the effects of two more mountain building episodes. The Lake District has been lifted up, eroded and has probably seen more marine sedimentation which has since been completely removed by the forces of erosion. The last episode, the Alpine mountain building, pushed the area up into a gentle dome. What we have now is the core of the once colossal Caledonian mountains, still forming impressive peaks and revealing the structures which explain their fiery origins.

Finally the mountains were sculpted by glaciers which covered the region during the Quaternary Ice Age, a relatively recent and short lived event but one which has had a dramatic effect on the character of this unique region.

Slate

A group of rocks known collectively as the Skiddaw Slates covers a large part of the northern Lake District. It requires no great expertise in geological mapping to trace its junction with the Borrowdale Volcanic Series; the rounded hills and peaks such as Skiddaw and Blencathra contrast markedly with the rugged topography produced by the volcanic rocks.

Consider for a moment where else in the British Isles you may have seen this familiar and prosaic rock. Perhaps Cornwall's majestic coastline comes to mind or the beautiful mountains of North Wales. This should be no surprise, slate is an inevitable product of the collision zone as two plates move towards each other. It is worth taking a look in a little detail how this extremely useful rock is formed.

True slate is composed largely of clay minerals which are compounds based around aluminium, silica and oxygen. They are typically formed by the routine weathering of other rocks, usually igneous or volcanic rocks. You may be familiar with Cornwall's china clay which is a product of the weathering of the Cornish granites. The clay minerals are then washed away and transported by rivers to the sea. Being very fine grained [strictly speaking less than 2 microns in diameter] they are often carried out by currents and gradually settle to the sea floor. Here they accumulate, eventually, due to pressure from above, forming rock.

The Skiddaw Slates were originally such sediments, deposited in quiet Ordovician seas around 500 million years ago, although there are features which suggest a location at or near a subduction zone where one plate was sliding underneath another. As slow movement of the plates continues these sediments are subject to increasing pressure, trapped in the jaws of a tectonic vice. Clay minerals naturally form flat crystals arranged in sheets. Under pressure they will begin to realign themselves at right angles to the force; it is this alignment that causes the characteristic slaty cleavage that can make the rock so useful for roofing. As the temperature and pressure builds so more changes become noticeable; new minerals may begin to form. It is not that the rock becomes chemically different, more that it rearranges its constituent elements in different combinations that are stable at different temperatures and pressures. One of the first "new" minerals to appear is chlorite.

Blencathra - with smooth, rounded shape typical of Skiddaw Slate country.

These processes are inevitably associated with mountain building episodes or orogenies and perhaps there is nothing better to chronicle the extraordinary events that have shaped our landscape than these ordinary rocks which are so well-known to anyone who has scrambled up peaks almost anywhere in the world.

The Skiddaw Slates may be anything up to 20 000 feet thick, the base has never been identified. When you think that the original sediment has been considerably compressed it gives some idea of the length of time it has taken to collect on the sea floor and then be gradually crushed and baked to the rock we see today. The name "Skiddaw Slate" is given to a collection of rocks; not all are slates. There are sediments which are much coarser grained, grits and sandstones. Some of these exhibit strange structures that are interpreted as the convolutions caused when huge masses of sediment tumble down a submarine slope, typically down the continental slope and perhaps into deep trenches caused by the buckling of the crust. These jumbled sandstones are often called "greywackes" and are to be found at a number of locations in the northern lakes. We know that such sediments are typical of the unstable boundary where an oceanic plate is being subducted.

The explanation given above may appear rather simple, but it is important to understand that the structures in the Skiddaw Group that geologists are faced with interpreting are anything but simple. To begin with the sediments were lithified [turned to rock] and uplifted to form land before the end of the Ordovician period. It was only during the Devonian period many millions of years later, in the final mountain building episode, that the characteristic slaty cleavage was formed. In the intervening time they were caught up in a turbulent volcanic episode when huge, deeply buried chambers of molten rock caused all manner of displacements in the surrounding rocks.

Some of the Lake District's slates have a rather different origin to that described above, although they have still been heated and compressed in the same manner. The difference lies in where the fine grained sediment came from. The famous green slates of Honister and Tilberthwaite are actually volcanic in origin. They are formed from ash and tuff erupted from a volcano, perhaps in a setting like the volcanic island arcs off the coast of Asia today. The ash fell on the sea, or perhaps a shallow lagoon, where it slowly drifted to the bottom, later to be caught in the grip of the colliding plates.

The Honister Pass showing a discarded pile of slate from the famous mine. This slate has been formed from volcanic ash that fell into water and was subsequently compressed by the enormous pressures generated as the tectonic plates collided.

Volcano!

Central Lakeland is composed of rocks known as the Borrowdale Volcanic Group. These rocks from the Ordovician period are around 450 million years old. The volcanics form the distinctive rugged peaks so popular with tourists and walkers. They were made in a relatively short time geologically speaking, perhaps in around 5 million turbulent years. The rocks we see today bear many of the hallmark features of products from volcanoes associated with "subduction zones", where one plate is sliding under another. There are many such volcanoes along the Pacific coast of Asia, often forming island arc systems just off the coast.

We know that the volcano that produced the Borrowdale Group was huge and that during its active life went through a number of phases, each of which has produced different deposits we see on the hills and fells today. It was certainly above sea level [remember there

Below: Volcanic rocks at Sour Milk Gill near Seathwaite in Borrowdale. These rocks were explosively erupted from a volcano. The ash and other debris settled in water and was compacted in layers. Such eruptions throw out a variety of material, look out for larger lumps in the layers and white streaks which may be bits of flattened pumice.

Above: The high, central core of the Lake District is composed of rocks from the Borrowdale Volcanic Series.

are many submarine volcanoes] and at or near the coast. Rather than being a mountain with a central vent it was probably a "caldera" with a number of vents. Caldera is the Spanish word for cauldron, derived from the Latin for a cooking pot. Underneath a volcano is typically a huge magma chamber. After magma escapes in a violent explosion this underground chamber may collapse, leaving a vast crater or caldera. The eruption of Santorini in the Mediterranean which devastated the Minoan civilisation left just such a feature. Naturally, such titanic earth movements have left a complicated legacy and geologists have spent many years trying to unravel the complex evidence presented by the rocks. There are still debates and disagreements but what I have outlined above is generally accepted. Although it may be difficult for the interested visitor to appreciate the geological history in detail, it is still fun to be able to pick out features of the rocks and understand what processes are responsible for their formation.

Lava or molten rock is the product many people first associate with volcanoes. Hypnotic sequences of lava flowing down hillsides from Mount Etna or cascading in a steaming frenzy into the ocean around Hawaii have been shown many times on television. Such eruptions are typical of volcanoes where the source material has what is known as a "basic" composition. Confusingly, this has nothing to do with pH level but means the lava has a relatively low silica content. This results in the lava being quite fluid. The first activity of the "Borrowdale volcano" was the eruption of such lavas and their solidified flows can be seen at many places in the Lake District, for example in the area around Brown Knotts near Ashness Bridge. This sort of volcanism can also be seen at many places on the Earth's crust today. As an oceanic plate slides or is subducted under a continental plate water is taken down to the "mantle", the layer underneath the crust. This has the effect of lowering the melting temperature of the mantle rock, which melts and buoyantly rises to the surface.

When lava is relatively rich in silica its physical characteristics are changed markedly; it becomes altogether more viscous and sticky. This has dramatic consequences for the lava is no longer able to flow smoothly out of the vents, instead these often become blocked by the quickly solidifying fluid. Huge pressures build up behind the vents and it probably comes as no surprise that the more explosive volcanoes are

Above: The Langdale Pikes - classic Borrowdale Volcanics territory. These mountains are largely composed of explosive volcanic products such as tuffs and ignimbrites which are rocks formed from the welded debris of pyroclastic flows that once tumbled down mountain sides.

Above: The stream at Stockdale, Longsleddale rushing over rhyolite lava. This is a crystalline rock similar to granite but rapid cooling has resulted in crystals too small for the naked eye.

associated with this type of lava which is produced as the basic lava melts and mixes with other rocks on its way to the surface. The second phase of the Borrowdale volcanics comprised such eruptions. When the pressure build up behind vents clogged with sticky lava got too much, violent explosions were the result, perhaps similar to the famous eruption of Mount St. Helens. The products of this sort of volcanism are very different. Instead of lava flows, huge quantities of ash and other debris are thrown into the air. As they fall to the ground deep layers of volcanic ash or tuff are formed. Some of the hot material gets welded into clumps like clinker from a fire. Again there are many examples of these sort of volcanic rocks in the Lake District.

Also common are what are known as "volcaniclastic" deposits, a grand sounding name for volcanic ash that has fallen in water and been subsequently laid down in layers as if it were "normal" sediment derived from the erosion of previous rocks. These deposits tell us that the vents of the Borrowdale volcano were surrounded by lakes or perhaps shallow water lagoons. The third phase of the Borrowdale sequence is usually defined by the formation of these rocks. Later on we will see where all these different types of deposits can be seen and appreciated.

More sedimentation

The volcanic activity died away towards the end of the Ordovician
period and the layers of ash, tuff and lava that had grown into at least
one mountain began to erode away. This has happened to many volcanic
islands in the past and will one day be the fate of the Hawaiian islands
and others that owe their existence to the Earth's hot spots.

The evidence in the rocks tells us that now the Lake District
was covered by a relatively shallow sea in which limestones, sandstones
and other sediments were deposited. There were some sporadic
outbursts of volcanic activity which extruded submarine lavas into the
sediments. This deposition continued for millions of years, building up
great thicknesses. Coupled with the converging plates and the gradual
destruction of the ocean floor this would have led to the development of
various basins divided by shallower regions. We can imagine occasional
earthquakes triggering underwater "landslides" [or turbidity currents]
into the deep basins.

Below: Tarn Hows.
The original layers [bedding] of these Silurian sediments dip at
a completely different angle to the cleavage caused by intense
compression. This shows that the original layers have been tightly
folded.

direction of cleavage
direction of bedding

Above: A piece of conglomerate found in a stream at Stockdale. Note the irregular shaped pebbles of pink rhyolite.

These late Ordovician and Silurian sediments make up much of the southern part of the Lake District. They rest unconformably on the Borrowdale Volcanics, meaning that they cut across the layers of the older rocks, clearly demonstrating that they were deposited on a previously eroded surface. Not only that, the first sediment we see from this phase is a conglomerate. The name of this type of rock provides a good description, they are composed of bits and pieces of eroded material, large and small bits all jumbled together. They typically form as beach deposits and so often represent the first sediments laid down as the sea encroaches over a previous area of land. The conglomerate contains pebbles of volcanic material, particularly lava which is more resistant to weathering than the ash and tuff. At places such as Stockdale in Longsleddale you can see this conglomerate with weathered bits of lava, inches away from the lava flow out of which it was eroded. To go from one state to the other took millions of years!

The deposition of the Windermere Supergroup, as this set of sediments is called, began around 450 million years ago. The reader may have wondered where these dates come from; how do we know the age of rocks? The only way to obtain absolute dates is by radio-isotope dating, a sophisticated technique that uses the known rate of decay of certain radioactive elements. This can only be done with igneous rocks, rocks that cooled from a molten state, and so began their life with a definite quantity of these elements. Geologists therefore have built up a series of time markers using these rocks; others, including all sedimentary ones have to be relatively dated.

Left: Graptolite remains in slate looking rather like miniature hacksaw blades. The tiny colonial creatures lived in the "teeth" of the saw and were connected by some sort of central canal. [Photo courtesy of Keswick Museum.]

This is where fossils come in. The Lake District is not one of the more well-known areas for fossil collecting; there are none in the volcanic rocks and although the slates were originally marine sediments, the strong compression and folding has tended to obliterate fossil remains. Additionally it is only the shallow seas that would have been rich in life. Nevertheless there are fossils that are found in Lake District sediments and one group in particular has been of immeasurable use to geologists, namely the graptolites.

Graptolites were unusual creatures, classified as hemi-chordates, with a rudimentary central canal, they were tiny colonial animals connected by a skeleton of collagen. Their spindly traces [see photo] are like delicate pressed plant remains on the surface of slate. Geologists have found them useful for two reasons. Firstly, since they floated near the surface of ancient seas, they were wide ranging and are found in all types of marine sedimentary rocks, including those formed in the deep abyssal regions. Secondly they evolved very quickly, enabling them to be used as zone fossils. If a particular species was only around for a relatively short time, then two geographically removed sedimentary layers which contain this fossil are known to be of roughly the same age. Using fossils like this enables geologists to correlate strata from one region to another, building up a picture of what was going on at that particular time across a wide area.

Mountain Building

It is tempting to think of the present mountains of the Lake District as
the eroded remnants of the once great mountain chain known as the
Caledonides. Unfortunately the picture is a good deal more complicated.
There were indeed volcanic mountains during the Ordovician period, but
once the volcanic activity had subsided the landscape was eroded flat and
the sea returned; as we have seen, depositing further sediments on the
worn down volcanic base. Although one of the main tenets of geology is
that the key to past events lies in the processes that are happening on the
Earth today, it should be remembered that the erosion of land surfaces
must have happened rather more quickly then than it does at the present
time. This is because land plants were in the early stages of development
and had not yet completely colonised the land. Indeed, remains of fossil
plants from the Ordovician show them to be tiny plants like liverworts
and mosses. They lacked conducting tissue and consequently were small
and restricted to environments with plentiful water.

An episode of mountain building is known as an orogeny. The
Caledonian orogeny was a complicated event, lasting many millions of
years and controlled by the convergence of tectonic plates. Throughout
the Ordovician period two continental masses known as Baltica and
Laurentia gradually moved together, Baltica moving roughly north-east

*Below: Tight folds in the Skiddaw Slates seen in an outcrop near
Buttermere church. The layers have obviously been tightly compressed
and the direction of the cleavage is at right angles to the direction of
the compression.*

Above: Small thrusts in a quarry at Mungrisdale. Here compression has caused the rocks to shear. The thrusts run diagonally across the picture from top left to bottom right.

and Laurentia south-west. The Iapetus Ocean was trapped between them, its southern margin being subducted under Baltica. The piece of crust we now call the Lake District was around this region, the north-west of Scotland on the opposing side of the ocean.

During the Silurian period the Iapetus Ocean continued to close, trapped between converging plates. Buckles in the crust again resulted in deep trenches and huge quantities of sediment accumulated. Eventually the ocean was squeezed out of existence and the sediment was folded by the huge tectonic vice into an extensive mountain range. The remnant volcanic rocks were caught in this also.

It is worth pausing here to give vent to our misgivings about these seemingly improbable scenarios which contradict our everyday experience of the world. The ancient Lakeland hills seem eternal. Year after year savage weather does little to alter their outline; yet we are asked to believe that huge volcanic mountains were worn down flat by these same processes we see today and that on top of this the sea laid down thousands of feet of sediment which were then formed into mountains of Himalayan proportions, only to be worn down again to expose the battered core of the volcanics. And all this associated with the destruction of a 2-3000 mile wide ocean! In the early days of the development of the theory of "plate tectonics" many scientists shared these misgivings, but gradually the evidence became incontrovertible that the distribution of land on the face of the Earth changes and that oceans are created and squeezed out of existence.

So, the challenge becomes to try to understand how these global tectonic events happen and to spot the tell-tale signs of the processes in the landscape. To begin with consider the big picture: the rocks of the Lake District have been folded. We can see these structures in the field [the geologist's term for the outdoors!], layers of rock once straight and horizontal now twisted and crumpled. Overwhelmingly the folds in the rocks are aligned in the same way, as if the pressure that produced them came from a NW-SE direction. This is entirely consistent with the proposal of one plate gradually moving towards another as outlined above. Next think of the folds themselves. We know that marine sediments are laid down in flat layers [a major exception being the turbidity current deposits we have met before]. When we see these layers folded and squashed it is obvious huge forces are involved. Rocks are generally hard and brittle, if I were able to squeeze rock between the jaws of a large vice, surely it would shatter? But what if the rocks were

deeply buried and heated to some extent? What about if the rate of compression were many times slower than even the most gradual turning of a vice? Perhaps then it is not surprising that layers of solid rock behave in an altogether more fluid manner and produce the sorts of shapes we now see exposed on the surface. Also, if we see a sedimentary rock, once in flat, horizontal layers, now

Right: Layered deposits of volcanic ash laid down in water. Note the shear that has offset the layers. This shear or small thrust was the result of compressional forces.

folded, it seems clear that the layers must also have been shortened; again entirely consistent with plates moving together.

Finally, rocks nearer the surface and undergoing compression [and tension] do behave in a brittle manner. This is the cause of the many "faults" and "thrusts" we see, cracks in the rocks where one side is displaced relative to the other. These add enormously to the complexity of the geological history.

Later on, in the gazetteer of places, we will look at some of the locations where these features can be seen.

Left: These slates between Buttermere and Crummock Water have been folded. It is not often that such folding can be seen. For one thing the folds are usually on a larger scale, often several kilometres across, so all we can see is tilted strata. Also the folding has given the rocks the pervasive slaty cleavage at right angles to the direction of compression, often obliterating traces of the original layers. The orientation of the cleavage is naturally vertical or nearly vertical, useful for the many trees whose roots are forced between the cleavage planes!

Right: Although the cleavage [preferred direction of splitting] in these rocks is clearly nearly vertical, the original layers can be seen to be folded in graceful curves [slightly above and left of centre]. Tilberthwaite quarry.

Intrusions

Many Lake District rocks are igneous in origin; meaning they have solidified from a molten state. As we have seen many of these have been extruded on the surface of the earth as lavas or intruded into cracks and fissures a little way below the surface. Some igneous rocks, however, were emplaced deep below the surface and we see them now due to millions of years of erosion. There is an easy way to distinguish between the two: when a lava flows onto the surface it cools quickly, leaving little time for crystals to grow. The rock is therefore fine grained and it is impossible to see the crystals with the naked eye. If molten rock cools deep in the Earth's crust it may take thousands of years to solidify, allowing plenty of time for crystals to grow. In these rocks it is easy to see the crystals. Remember that igneous rocks consist of a collection of different minerals and the melts from which they form have complicated compositions. Different minerals crystallize out at different temperatures, hence the pattern of interlocking crystals we see in rocks such as granite.

Coarse grained intrusive igneous rocks like granite are commonly associated with destructive plate margins. As one plate is forced down underneath the other heat is generated and the rocks begin to melt. Gradually the molten rock begins to move upwards, and there

Above: An igneous dyke cutting across slates in the Caldew Valley.

has been much discussion how this happens. It seems obvious that the molten rock is more buoyant and will migrate upwards if possible, but it is perhaps less obvious how this actually happens. First of all we should say that only a small fraction of a rock need melt for the whole mass to become mobile, particularly under great pressure, and it is thought that surrounding rock may simply flow around the migrating melt. It may also be forced through cracks and fissures. Underneath the Lake District is a large body of such igneous rock, mainly granite, known as the Lake District batholith. The granites we see exposed at Shap, Skiddaw, Ennerdale and Threlkeld are all connected to this huge mass. Some intrusions seem to have cooled in the Ordovician period while others are Lower Devonian in age.

Other igneous intrusions that we see are on a more intimate scale. Sills and dykes are sheet like bodies that have been forced, when molten, along cracks and fissures in surrounding rocks. Many of these are associated with the Borrowdale Volcanic Series and some with the larger scale intrusions. Traditionally sills are classified as intrusions that run parallel to the natural bedding planes or layers of the rocks into which they are intruded, while dykes cut across those layers.

Above: On the very left of the picture the Threlkeld granite intrusion has pushed up the overlying Borrowdale volcanics. The granite was quarried in the late 19th century and 20th century for use as railway ballast.

Above: The Ennerdale Granophyre at Sourmilk Gill on the edge of Buttermere. A granophyre is simply a granite with smaller crystals [technically medium grained] and the beautiful pink colour is well exposed in this charming waterfall. This granitic pluton is thought to be about 1100 metres thick, 14 km long and 4 km wide - yet is only one layer of the Lake District batholith!

It is thought to be Ordovician in age, well over 400 million years old, associated with the Borrowdale volcanics. It is probably the result of partial melting of the crust in a subduction zone.

Finally we must mention the Carrock Fell igneous complex. This is a sequence of igneous rocks quite different in composition from the other major intrusions. Many of the rocks here are "basic" in composition, that is to say relatively low in silica. The coarse grained variety of such rocks is known as gabbro. The sequence is probably Ordovician in age and was forced into the Skiddaw Group before the closure of the Iapetus Ocean and the deformations of the Caledonian Orogeny. Chemically the rocks are related to the sort of basalt that the ocean floor is made of and which can be melted or partially melted during the subduction of an oceanic plate.

Granite

Granite is one of the most familiar and recognisable rock types, and large granite bodies or "plutons" are common all over the Earth's continents. The composition of granite is different to that of the basalt from which the oceanic crust is made in that it contains a good deal more silica. This is made manifest by the presence of quartz in granite whose clear or milky crystals can easily be seen by the naked eye. It is obvious from examining a piece of granite that it is a mixture of different minerals, these too are clearly visible. This helps explain, in part, how granite forms.

   Along a subduction zone where one plate is sliding beneath another there will be some melting at the bottom of the crust. This melting will be partial and it is the silica rich minerals that will tend to melt first: thus the composition of the melt will be different from that of the rock it derives from.

   Geologists have long thought that it would then take hundreds of thousands, if not millions of years for the granitic melt to rise through the overlying rocks, gradually forcing them to flow around the ascending pluton. More recent research suggests this may not necessarily be the case. Some scientists now think the melt could form in hundreds of years, rise through fissures and then spread out along planes of weakness again in hundreds of or perhaps a few thousand years. This emplacement would typically be several kilometres below the surface.

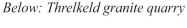

Below: Threlkeld granite quarry

Mining and Quarrying

As we have seen, igneous rocks are chemically very complex. The molten magmas from which they form contain many elements in different proportions. The most abundant are usually silicon, oxygen, potassium, sodium, calcium, magnesium and iron. As the melt cools these bond to form silicate minerals such as quartz and feldspar. Naturally the more reactive metals such as sodium, potassium and magnesium bond first, forming minerals which precipitate out. Towards the end of the cooling process less reactive metals such as copper, lead and tin tend to be concentrated in the remaining fluid. These watery fluids may be forced under pressure into cracks and fissures in the surrounding rocks. This is why we find deposits of such metals around granite intrusions like those in Cornwall and the Lake District.

There has been much debate over the mechanisms and sequence of the formation of the Lake District mineral deposits, but the above general outline remains true. Recent research has suggested that the main metalliferous deposits may be associated with the final stages of the great Ordovician volcanic episode. Many of the world's metal sulphide ores were formed in submarine locations from hot fluids circulating in unconsolidated sediments on the ocean floor or in volcanic deposits.

Below: Old waste heaps in Coppermines Valley near Coniston

Note the layers of volcanic tuff in the centre of this picture. This is a small waterfall at the beginning of Coppermines Valley near Coniston. The mineral veins were probably deposited by hydrothermal fluids circulating in such underwater volcanic sediments.

Copper mining in the Lake District began on a truly commercial scale in the 16th century guided by mining experts from Germany. It first developed in the area around Keswick but later in the century the rich deposits around Coniston began to be worked. The main mineral ore was chalcopyrite or copper iron sulphide. To those with a little knowledge of chemistry it should not be surprising that this mineral is associated with volcanic activity. The hot fluids from which this mineral precipitated were typically forced along largely vertical or near vertical joints formed by tension in the crust due to the upward movement of molten magma. Thus many of the copper mines had to be very deep. At Coniston these eventually went down over 1600 feet.

Production of copper peaked in the mid 19th century but soon after began to decline, finishing altogether in the latter part of the century. The mines had become too deep to be economical in face of cheap imported ore. Today Coppermines Valley near Coniston gives some idea of the scale of the industry at its height in the 1850s.

Sulphides of lead and zinc are often associated with those of copper and these too have been mined in Cumbria since the 16th century.

It is quite likely that lead ore was mined by the Romans, given their penchant for lead plumbing. It is a very easy metal to smelt and work requiring quite low temperatures to separate it from the ore.

The other great natural resource from the Lakeland rocks is of course slate. It should be remembered that this is slate produced by the compression of volcanic sediments, tuff and ash that was thrown out in great quantities by violent volcanic eruptions and a large proportion of which settled in lakes and shallow seas, later to be caught in the great Caledonian mountain building episode. The two main locations for the quarrying of high grade roofing slate were Honister and Tilberthwaite. You can tour the old mines at Honister and visit a museum. The vast old quarries at Tilberthwaite give some idea of the huge quantities that were produced.

Below: The ruins of Tilberthwaite quarry near Langdale. Slate has been quarried in the Lake District for hundreds of years. The earliest records of quarrying date from the 13th century but it would have been going on well before this. As well as for roofing slate was used as a building stone and for decorative purposes.

More Erosion

As we have seen, just over 400 million years ago, at the beginning of the Devonian period, the Lake District became part of a great mountain chain that included Scotland and Scandinavia. The Iapetus Ocean had disappeared and two continents that geologists have called Laurentia and Baltica joined to form a new super-continent. The Devonian was a time when plants diversified and proliferated, but at the beginning they were still relatively undeveloped. The mountain range, therefore, cannot have been densely covered in vegetation, even at lower levels. This means that erosion was probably quite rapid.

We can imagine a picture of high mountains with fast rivers carrying eroded material to the plains below. When such rivers reach the plains the sudden change of gradient slows them down and they are unable to continue carrying much of their load. Thus great fans of pebbles, sand and other detritus built up on the edges of the mountain range.

In the Lake District the evidence for this process is centred around Mell Fell near Ullswater. Here we find the Mell Fell Conglomerate. A conglomerate is a type of sedimentary rock that we often see at the start of a sedimentary cycle. It comprises of a mixture of coarse material, often pebbles, surrounded by finer material such as sand or gravel. Typically they are formed from beach deposits, hence the reason they often signify a return to marine conditions and subsequent marine sedimentation. The Mell Fell Conglomerate really is a varied mixture with the pebbles having a rounded character showing they have been transported by water. The size of some of the pebbles shows just how powerful the rivers that carried them must have been, perhaps an indicator of the important part that storms play in the erosion of our landscape. The pebbles have been shown to derive from Silurian sediments, Skiddaw slates and from the Borrowdale volcanics and geologists think that they were deposited in a number of river fans which coalesced.

Gradually the mountains were eroded away and by around 350 million years ago the sea had returned; the great Caledonian mountains of the Lake District had been worn flat! In this book I have tried to focus on what can be seen and appreciated by the interested visitor to the fells and the Mell Fell Conglomerate is a good indication that rapid erosion of the mountains took place in Devonian times. But how are we going to appreciate that the mountain range was subsequently below sea level 50 million years later? To do this we need to look at a general geological map of the area. If you do you will see that the Lake District is ringed by Carboniferous deposits – it's as if they have been cleared away to reveal a window of what's underneath, and that is exactly what has happened. The Carboniferous sediments once covered the entire region. They too have been subsequently worn away!

It is thought that the sea returned again during the Cretaceous period when the great Chalk seas covered much of Britain. More sediments were deposited but the area was raised again by the earth movements that accompanied the Alpine mountain building phase. Thus the Cretaceous sediments have also been removed. What we are left with is the hard, mangled core of a once great mountain range.

Above: The Mell Fell Conglomerate exposed on the road around Ullswater near Pooley Bridge. The mixture of small and very large material shows the river must have dropped its load very quickly. These pebbles were eroded from the great Caledonian mountains.

Final Touches

Glaciation

Much of the Lake District's dramatic scenery was produced in the geological period known as the Pleistocene, a short and recent period that stretched from around 1.8 million years ago to about 10 000 years before the present. This was the age of world wide glaciations, when much of the northern hemisphere was, at times, covered by extensive and thick ice sheets. In Britain the ice reached about as far south as Bristol.

Four major periods of Pleistocene glaciations have been identified with warmer interglacial periods in between. The glacial features of the Lake District are largely the work of the last of these, the Devensian glaciation which ended around 30 000 years ago. In upland areas ice collected at the head of valleys gradually flowing down valleys in glaciers which eventually joined the ice sheets covering the lowlands. The legacy of this ice on the landscape is basically of two varieties, features which are the result of erosion and those that are the result of the deposition of eroded material.

Below: Looking north from Grasmere - a typical U-shaped valley blocked at the end by glacial moraine forming Dunmail Raise.

Above: In the Glenderaterra valley west of Blencathra. This is Skiddaw Slate territory, but the large rocks and boulders at the top of the slope are from the Borrowdale volcanics. They are glacial "erratics", carried and then dumped here by the ice sheet which extended from the central core of the Lake District mountains to the south. It is features like this which help us to work out the direction of ice movement.

The erosional features we see are usually the work of valley glaciers. The glaciers widened and deepened their valleys into the characteristic U-shape. The interlocking spurs of land typical of the valley of a meandering river were truncated, and as the major valleys were deepened, tributary valleys were left hanging at their side, often the site of waterfalls today. The heads of the valleys where the glaciers originated were hollowed out leaving bowl shaped "corries" often occupied now by small lakes or tarns. Back to back or side to side development of corries has led to precipitous edges or arêtes.

The lakes themselves, of course, have formed in the over-deepened valley bottoms, often dammed by material dropped by the glaciers as the gradient levelled out. Other deposits or glacial moraines are generally quite easy to identify; many valleys have irregular hummocks where material has been dropped by an ice sheet and subsequently smoothed by its passing.

Superimposed drainage

Looked at from above the valleys, rivers and lakes of the National Park can be seen to radiate in all directions from the central uplands. Given a little thought, this may seem surprising: the structures in the rocks of the Lake District overwhelmingly trend in a NE-SW direction, a result of compression from the NW and SE. One might have expected the rivers to pick out these structures and this direction. Many geography and geology text books have explained this apparent anomaly, for it is a classic example of a phenomenon known as "superimposed drainage". In the millions of years following the volcanic activity and clash of plates which caused the Caledonian mountains the Lake District, as we have seen, was eroded and covered by layer upon layer of later sediments. In the Tertiary era around 15-20 million years ago another collision of plates [effectively Europe and Africa] gave rise to the Alpine mountain range. While removed from the centre of these deformations, the rocks of Britain were subject to stresses transmitted through the hard, ancient "basement" rocks which everywhere underlie later deposits. Thus the Lake District became a gentle dome with rivers naturally radiating from its centre. Gradually the layers of sediment were worn away and the rivers began to cut into the underlying strata, superimposing their radial pattern on rocks with a very different orientation.

Below: Ullswater, a typical ribbon lake formed by glacial meltwater in a valley overdeepened by the scouring action of a glacier.

Gazetteer of Places

The places mentioned in the gazetteer are not intended to form any sort of itinerary, they merely serve as examples of what to look for when out enjoying the Lake District scenery, although I have attempted some sort of order for the locations, starting in the north-east of the park and working southwards. For anyone wanting to look seriously and in detail at the geology I would recommend the Geologists' Association Guide No. 2 "The Lake District" and "Exploring Lakeland – Rocks and Landscapes" by the Cumberland Geological Society. Both organisations have web sites where the books can be ordered. Grid references are given for each location, usually where a photograph was taken or at the feature referred to.

Caldew Valley, Mosedale [page 11]
The River Caldew now flows in a typical U-shaped valley widened by a valley glacier. It is cut into Skiddaw Slates but also shows volcanic dykes, sheets of lava that were pushed along planes of weakness in the slates. All this happened deep underground, the lava coming from a huge chamber of molten magma to the north which now forms Carrock Fell. [NY 336325]

School House Quarry, Mungrisdale [page 24]
When I visited, the quarry was fenced off, but the feature I was interested in was quite visible. If you examine the photograph on page 24 you will see the slates seem to have sheared along two lines [strictly planes]. These are small scale thrusts, fractures in the rocks formed as they tried to accommodate the huge stresses as the Caledonian mountains were being squeezed up. Faults are also fractures that can easily be spotted although they are usually nearer the vertical and often caused by tension rather than compression. [NY 364305]

Glenderaterra Valley [page 10]
This is a good place for a broad view of things. It is deep in Skiddaw Slate territory, the smooth, rounded shape of the hills and the scree littered on the valley sides all testify to this. To the north is the Skiddaw granite intrusion and if you examine the slates as you walk up the valley you may notice them change. Different minerals begin to occur, visible firstly as little spots. This is due to the slates being heated and

metamorphosed as the hot granite pushed them aside. The view towards Derwent Water is impressive, revealing the more craggy mountains composed of Borrowdale volcanics. Notice the valley of St. John's Vale. Valleys often follow the course of important faults and this is no exception. [NY 302257]

Threlkeld Mining Museum
This friendly little museum run by volunteers is the ideal place to gain an overview of Lake District geology. There is an excellent 3D model and lots of rock samples. Threlkeld granite was quarried here and used as road stone and railway ballast. [NY 327247]

Ashness Bridge *[above]*
Ashness Bridge is a pretty, often busy, spot popular with photographers. Here the water tumbles over volcanic ashes, explosively erupted by an Ordovician volcano. Higher up in the valley below on Brown Knotts are lava flows. Lava is crystalline and therefore often very hard. You cannot see the crystals with the naked eye because, having been extruded on the surface, the lava cooled very quickly which only allowed small crystals to grow. Lava layers alternating with bands of volcanic ash often produces a stepped topography, as the harder lava is more resistant to erosion.
[NY 270197]

Aira Force *[top next page]*
Waterfalls are always popular and Aira Force will not disappoint! The pretty Aira Beck cascades 70 feet over andesite lava. Vigorous streams

often produce waterfalls when they encounter a more resistant rock layer. This type of lava is typical of the sort produced in an oceanic subduction zone.

[NY 400205]

Buttermere

The church at Buttermere *[below]* is built on a roche moutonée, a rock smoothed by the passage of a glacier. The rock is from the Skiddaw Group and shows tight folding of the strata. Where Sourmilk Gill enters Buttermere [NY 173164] there is a small, but delightful, waterfall over the Ennerdale Granophyre. This is a rock very similar to granite and was intruded into rocks of the Skiddaw Group during the Ordovician, probably associated with the Borrowdale volcanics. [NY 176170]

Seathwaite [page 16]

The footpath that ascends along the side of Sour Milk Gill is a classic location to see "volcaniclastic" sediments. These are rocks formed when volcanic ash from violent eruptions falls on water and settles in layers as do "normal" sediments composed of weathered sand, silt and clay particles. Look out for graded bedding, where larger particles have settled first in the water and grade into smaller particles. [photo next page] [NY 233122]

Above: Borrowdale near Seathwaite. In the foreground are layered volcanic ashes deposited in water.

Honister Pass [page 15]
The famous slates here are again composed of volcanic ashes that have settled in water. Their strong cleavage or preferred direction of splitting is a product of the tremendous compression during the mountain building. [NY 225136]

White Moss [page 44]
With wonderful views over Grasmere and Rydal Water, White Moss is a good place to appreciate the glacial heritage of the Lake District. Irregular glacial moraines litter the valleys and provide dams for the picturesque lakes. The road out of Grasmere towards Thirlmere follows a very broad U-shaped valley across the moraine deposits of Dunmail Raise. [page 36]
The rocks of White Moss itself are volcanic tuffs with good exposures to examine on the top and in a quarry by the car park.
[NY 347067]

Langdale
Langdale epitomizes so much that is typical of Lake District geology and scenery. The broad U-shaped valley of Great Langdale has been gouged by a glacier through volcanic ashes, tuffs and ignimbrites; so called "pyroclastic" deposits from a violent phase of the eruptions. There are lava flows too, providing horizons somewhat more resistant to erosion.

The flat, wide valley floor bears a coating of moraine, hummocky in places, dropped by the slowly moving glaciers. Waterfalls tumble down the steep sides of the "over-deepened" valleys.

The western end of Great Langdale follows the centre or axis of a major anticline or upward facing fold. Rocks in the very centre of such a fold tend to be stretched: this tension leads to cracks which are exploited by rivers and so anticlinal axes are often found in valley floors. Climb up the hills either side of Great Langdale and you should see the rock layers dipping or sloping away from the line of the valley. [NY 327048]

Tilberthwaite

Tilberthwaite was once one of the great quarrying centres of the Lake District. The Tilberthwaite Tuffs are derived from volcanic ash that settled in shallow lakes or maybe on the side of a volcano and subsequently removed and re-deposited by rivers. The later compression during the mountain building episode turned the fine grained tuffs into a slate of considerable commercial value. It has been used for building and ornamental work all over the country and many other parts of the world. The disused quarries are very impressive and give some idea of the huge quantities of slate once worked. [NY 304011]

Below: Tilberthwaite quarry. This huge chasm is the result of many years slate quarrying. It is easy to discern the direction of the cleavage!

Above: Looking from White Moss towards Rydal Water. The rock in the foreground is volcanic tuff.

Tarn Hows [see page 20]

Around the level of the lake at Tarn Hows the rocks are some of the later deposits in the Borrowdale Volcanic Series. A little climb above these however are Silurian sediments from the Windermere Supergroup. Between the two is an unconformity, that is to say that the sediments were deposited in a shallow sea on top of the eroded remains of the volcanic rocks. Both types of rocks were later folded into the Caledonian mountains. There is an outcrop of Silurian sediments behind the small disabled parking area to the east of the main car park. This outcrop shows an interesting feature that requires a little explaining.

Sediments are deposited in layers. With marine sediments like we have here, the layers were originally flat and horizontal, being built up on the sea floor. When the sediments were later compressed the layers were, of course, folded. As we have seen, the compression also resulted in a slaty cleavage being formed as the flat, clay minerals aligned themselves at right angles to the direction of the pressure. Thus the direction of the cleavage, or the way the rock splits, is also at right angles to the direction of the compression and remains uniformly so. The rock strata, however, follow their contorted pattern and sometimes we can see the layers of the rock distinct from the cleavage, and this is what we find at Tarn Hows. In this outcrop the original sedimentary layers lie in a different direction to the cleavage. [SD 331998]

Coppermines Valley [see page 31]

Once one of Britain's most important copper mining areas, large scale production at the Bonsor mine stopped in 1895. The ore that was mined here is chalcopyrite or copper iron sulphide. The peak year for copper production at Coniston was 1856 when over three and a half thousand tons of copper ore were produced. The mine at Bonsor was very deep, eventually reaching down 1600 feet.

The path to Coppermines Valley passes through an interesting succession of volcanic deposits. The small waterfall just before the valley opens out flows over bedded tuffs. You may have noticed a number of pictures of rocks in flowing water in this book; this is not just a testament to the amount of running water in the Lake District but also to the fact that the cleansing action of the water produces good exposures of the rocks! [SD 294980]

Above: On the path to Coppermines Valley. At first glance a jumbled sequence of volcanic rocks! But notice right in the middle a block with lighter patches. This is "eutaxitic" texture and the light bits are blocks of pumice that have been flattened by compression. Pumice can be thought of as solidified volcanic froth.

Longsleddale [see page 19]

The course of Brow Gill at Stockdale in Longsleddale provides one of the classic locations of Lake District geology. Such locations are where geologists have been able to describe in detail the succession of rocks from a particular geological age and perhaps gathered information, such as from the fossil record, that has enabled them and others to correlate rock strata in different locations.

At Stockdale we see the first Silurian sediments that were deposited on the eroded landscape of the Borrowdale Volcanics. Fossil graptolites have been found in the shales here [although I didn't find any!] and you may find pieces of conglomerate that represent the first beach deposits as the Silurian sea covered the Borrowdale landscape, including in its matrix pieces of volcanic rock previously eroded.

Further upstream we see the Stockdale Rhyolite, a lava erupted during the latter stages of the volcanic sequence. By now you should be able to recognise this hard, pinkish rock! [NY 493057]

Glossary

Batholith – a large mass of igneous rock, usually granite, originally lying deep underground.

Caldera – a crater formed when an explosive volcano erupts.

Cleavage – the preferred direction of splitting of rocks like slate, caused by compression and alignment of clay minerals.

Continental shelf – the area of relatively shallow ocean around continents; part of the continental crust rather than oceanic crust.

Crust – the outer layer of the Earth, composed of two types, continental and oceanic crust.

Fault – a plane of weakness in the crust where movement has occurred, often the result of tensional forces.

Folding – the deformation of rock layers caused by compression.

Geological period – geological time is divided into periods defined by the assemblages of fossils that are present.

Granite – a common coarse grained igneous rock whose composition reflects that of the continental crust.

Greywacke – a type of sandstone typically with structures that show transportation in fast flowing currents down the continental slope bordering the continental shelf.

Iapetus Ocean – the name given to an ancient ocean that closed as plates of the Earth's crust converged.

Igneous rock – rock that has cooled from a molten state.

Intrusion – a body of igneous rock that has been forced into surrounding rock.

Island arc – a chain of volcanic islands that forms from lava erupting from a subduction zone.

Lava – molten rock that is extruded on the surface of the Earth.

Magma – molten rock.

Mantle – the layer of the Earth beneath the crust, nearly 2000 miles thick.

Mineral – a naturally occurring chemical compound; most rock forming minerals are silicates.

Orogeny – a mountain building episode when the coming together of plates compresses and folds layers of rock trapped between them.

Plate tectonics – the science of the movement of plates of the Earth's crust.

Sedimentary rock – rock formed from the deposition of eroded particles of other rocks.

Sills and dykes – sheets of igneous rock intruded into surrounding rocks, either parallel to the layers [sills] or crossing the layers [dykes].

Slate – fine grained sediment that has been compressed and given a cleavage or preferred direction of splitting.

Subduction zone – where one plate of the Earth's crust is forced down underneath another.

Turbidity current – a swirling mass of sediment tumbling down the continental slope.

Further reading and bibliography

Books
Geology Explained in the Lake District - Robert Prosser, Fineleaf Editions

Geologists' Association Field Guide No.2 - The Lake District

Exploring Lakeland, Rocks and Landscapes - The Cumberland Geological Society

Beneath the Lakeland Fells - The Cumbria Amenity Trust Mining History Society, Red Earth Publications

Websites
www.lake-district.gov.uk [provides an excellent educational factsheet]

www.rocksafoot.com [another useful summary]

www.naturalengland.org.uk [has a county by county guide to England's geology]

There are a number of sites about geology in general; a couple worth visiting are:

www.geology.com [an American site but loads of information]

www.bgs.ac.uk [official site of the British Geological Survey - lots of educational material]